Sip

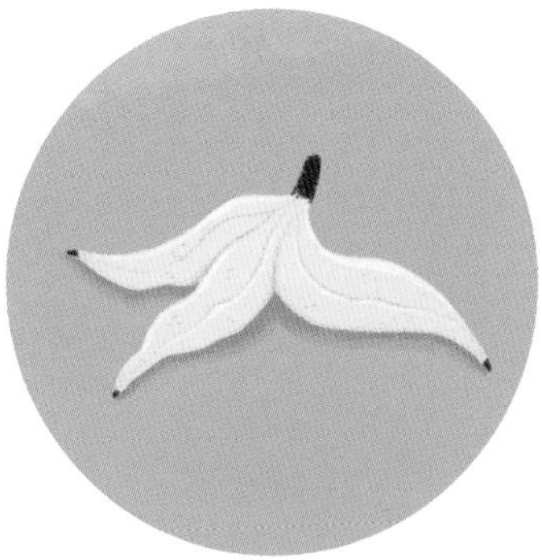

Rachel Menzies

Illustrated by Lucy Boden

Schofield&Sims

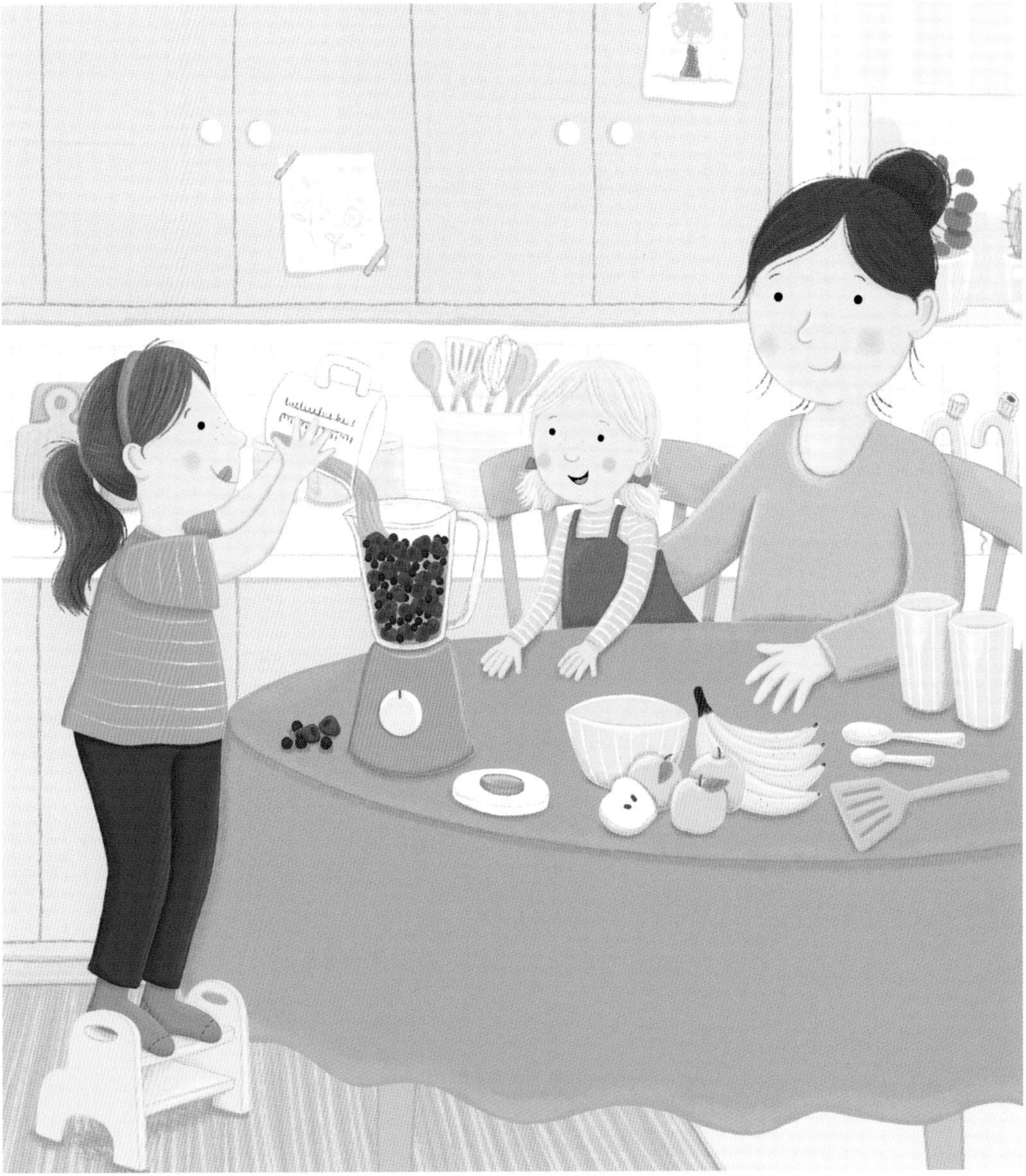

tip

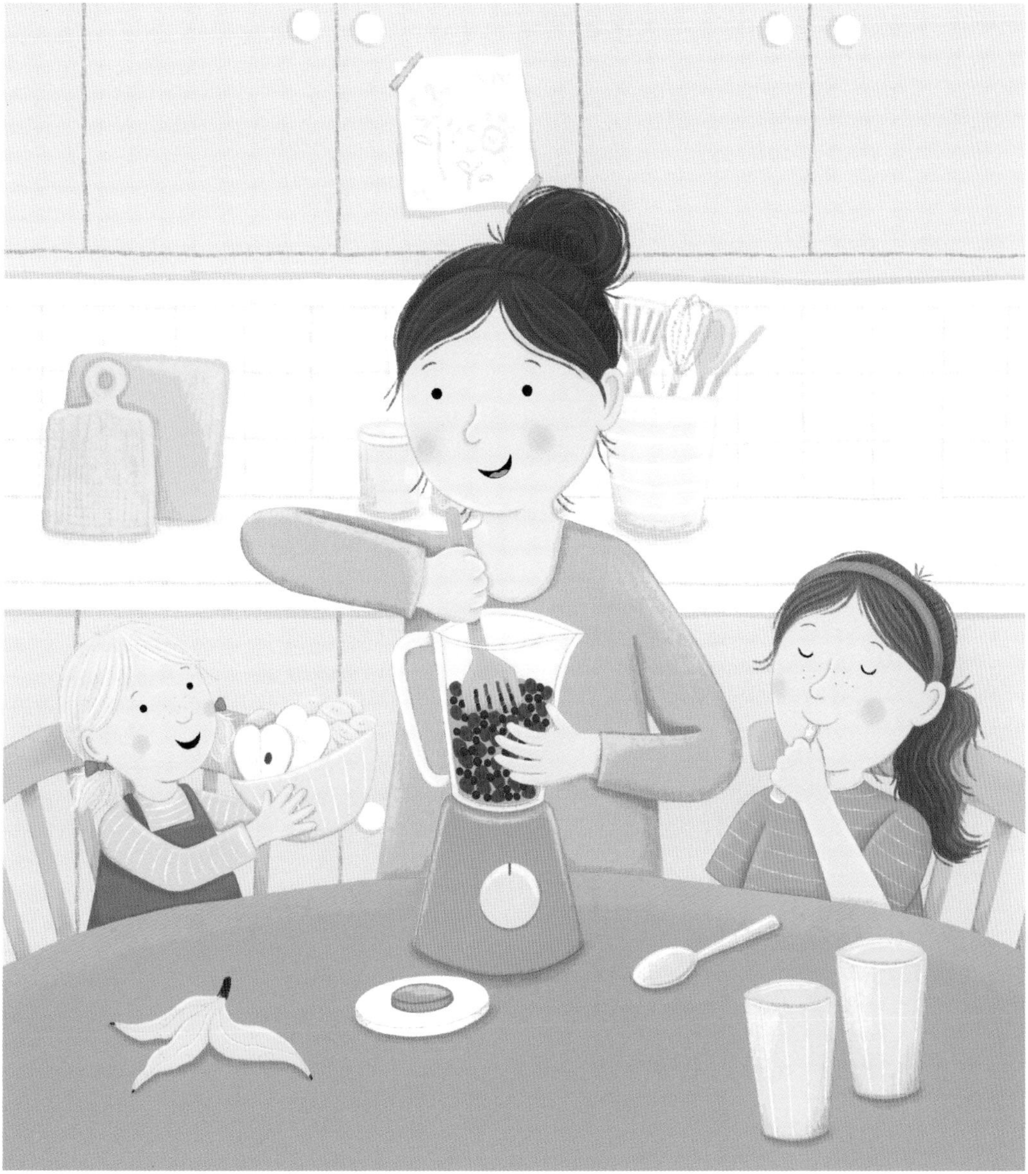

pat

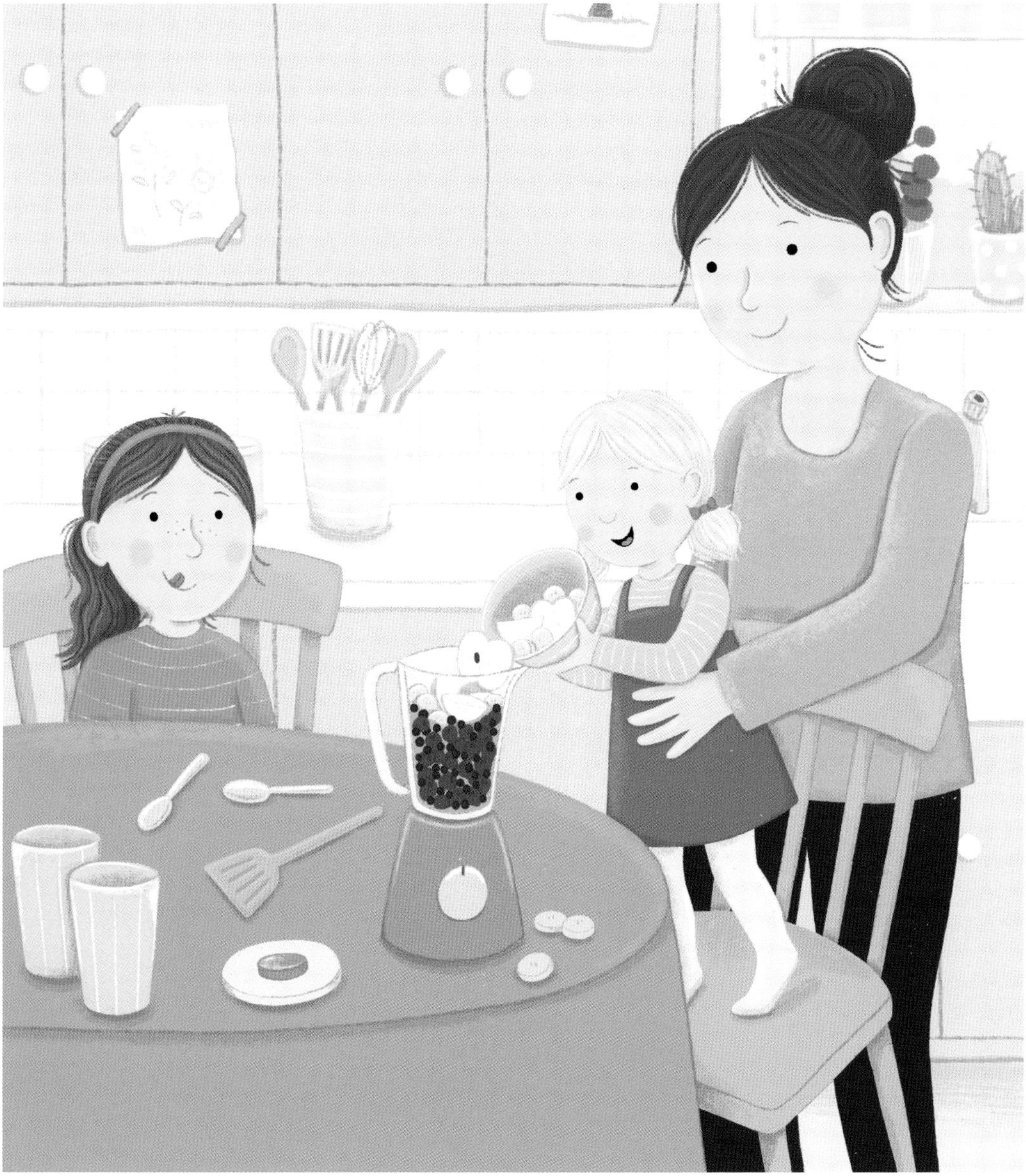

tip

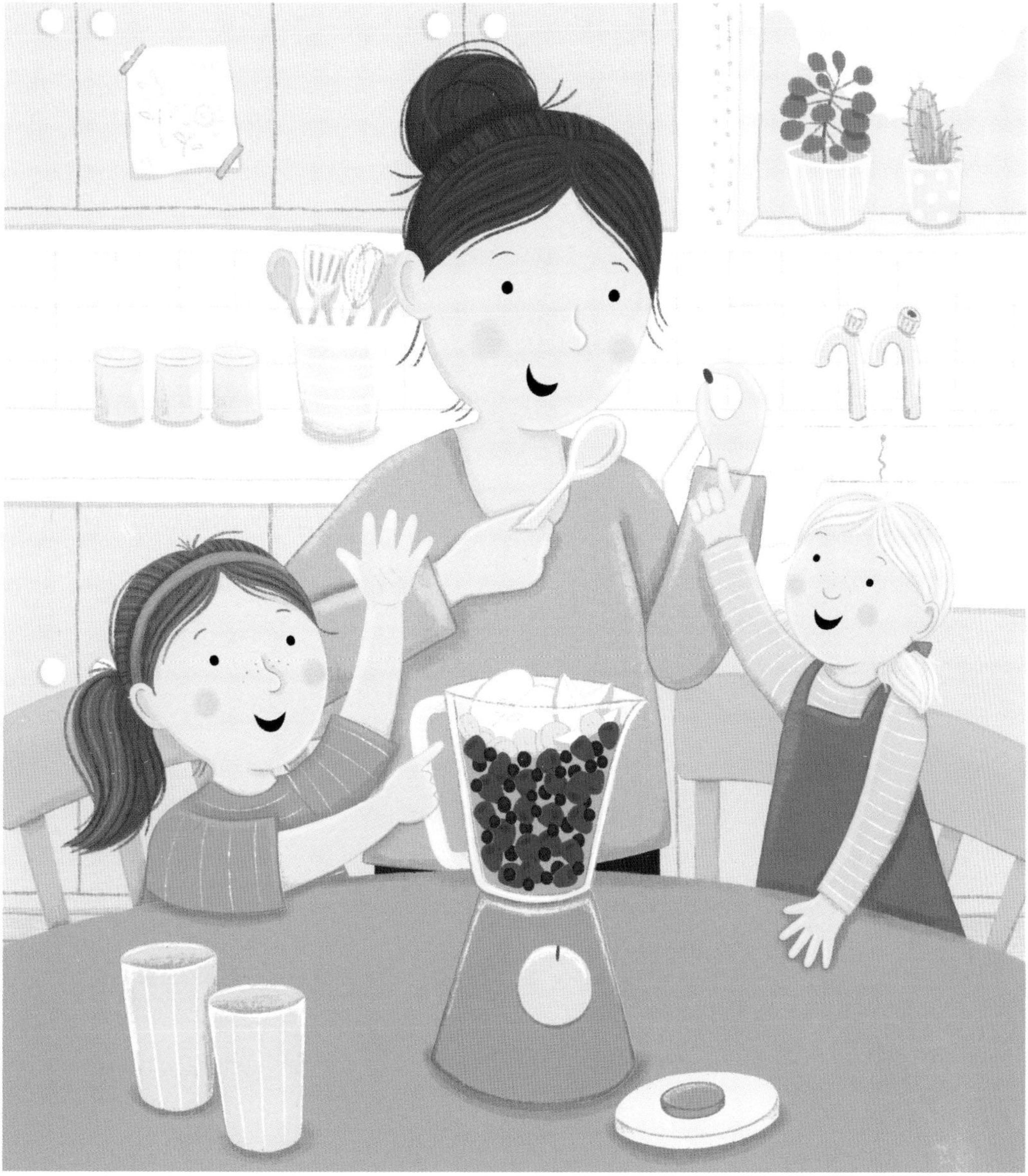

pip

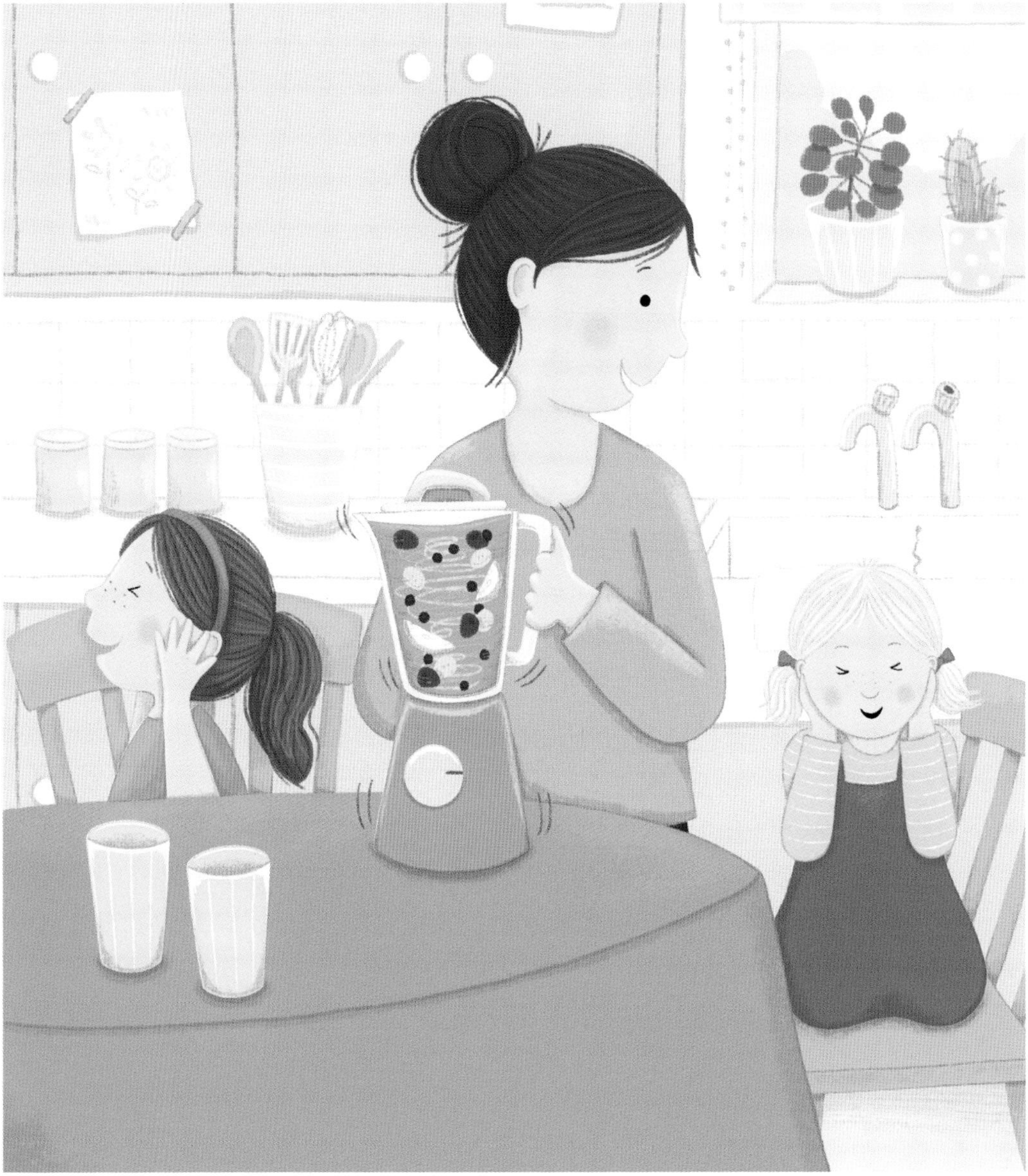

din

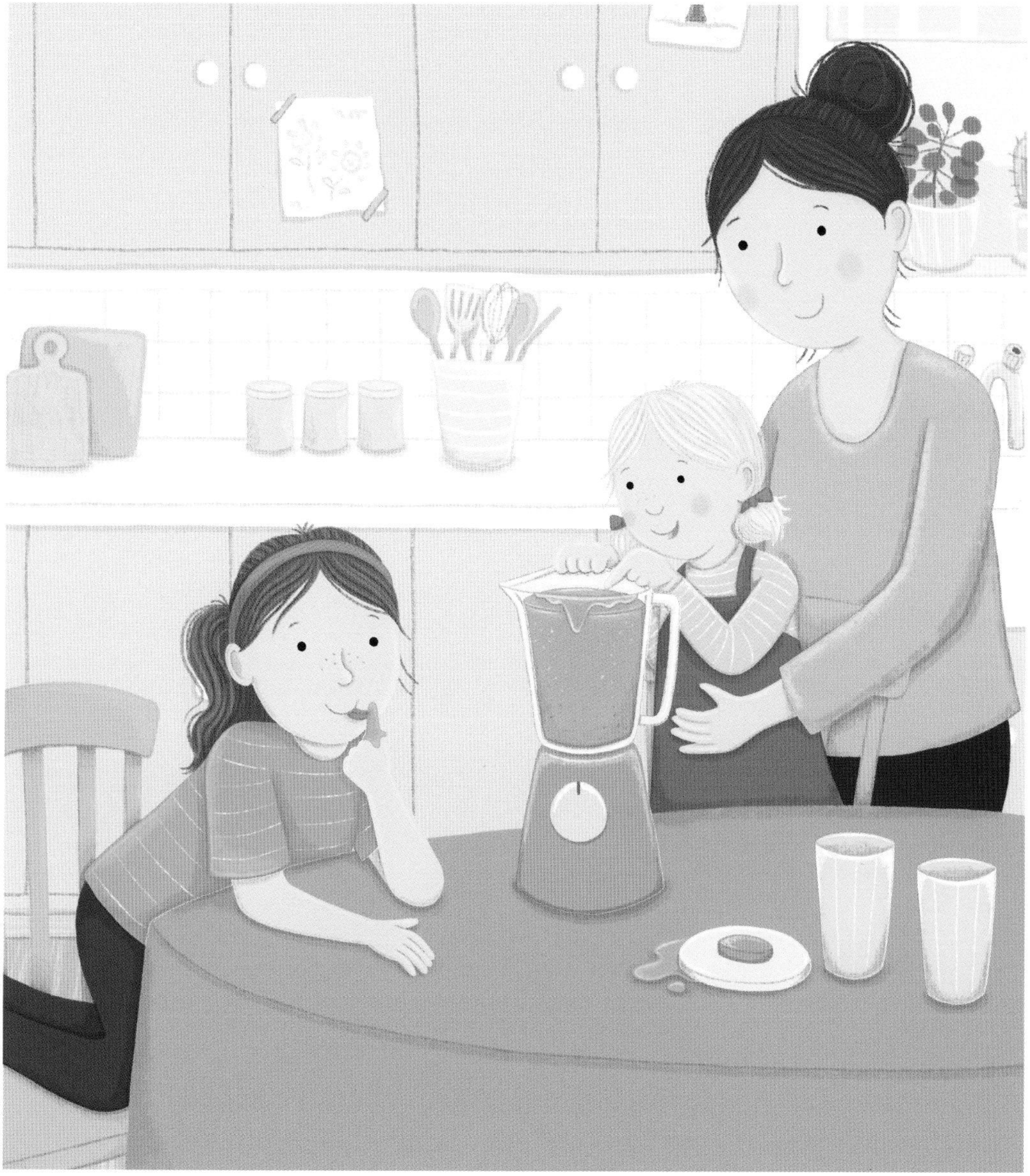

dip

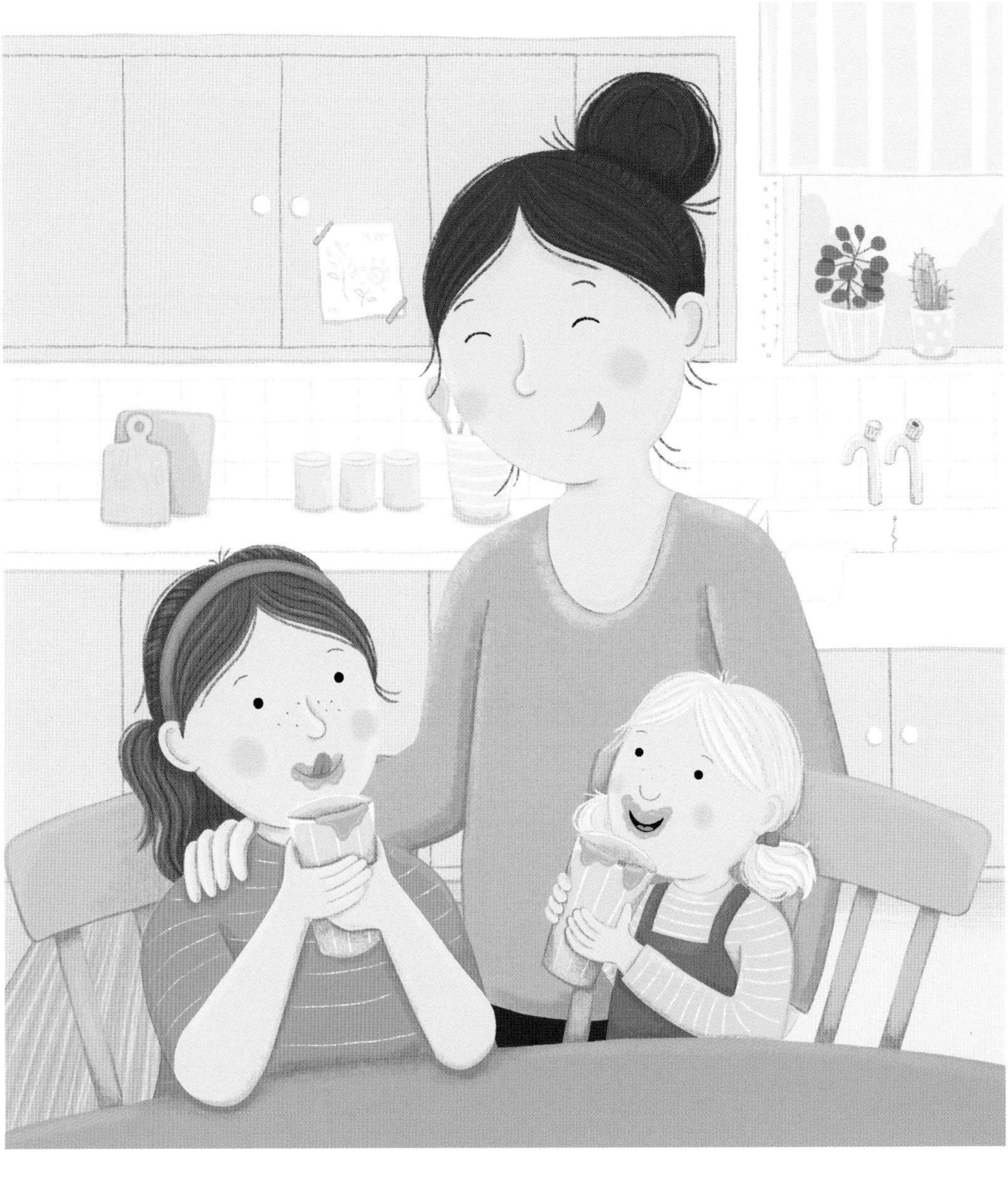

sip